THE COLOURS AND MARKINGS OF HORSES

DIANNE E. PACKER
B.Sc., Ph.D

and

TALIB M. ALI
B.V.Sc., Ph.D.

FARMING PRESS LTD
Wharfedale Road
Ipswich, Suffolk,
United Kingdom.

ACKNOWLEDGEMENTS

The Royal College of Veterinary Surgeons for permission to quote them as the authority whose recommendations are given in this book.

Major D. H. Witherington MRCVS of The Jockey Club and Mr H. Anderson of Weatherbys for the horse identification document.

Professor Clifford Formston, formerly Professor of Surgery and Vice Principal of the Royal Veterinary College, for the elucidation of some points of contention.

Colleagues at the Faculty of Veterinary Medicine, Tripoli for their encouragement.

British Library Cataloguing in Publication Data

Packer, Dianne
The colour and markings of horses.
1. Horses——Color 2. Animal marking
I. Title II. Ali, Talib M.
636.1'0892799 SF289.5

ISBN 0-85236-156-4

First published 1985
ISBN 0 85236 156 4

Typeset by Galleon Photosetting, Ipswich
Reproduced and printed by Acolortone Ltd, Ipswich

INTRODUCTION

The colour of the horse is perhaps the most obvious characteristic of the individual animal. A description of the coat colour and any markings is, together with height and age, a means of identifying individual animals. In many countries such descriptions are required when animals are registered with breed associations and a breed registration certificate gives details of coat colour, markings, adult height and foaling date. Indeed registration requirements for many breeds include restrictions on colour and there are some associations which register animals of a particular colour irrespective of type as in the case of the Palomino and American Albino.

Often when horses are bought and sold the animal must be given a certificate of veterinary soundness and on these documents the animal is identified by colour, markings and height. Horses must also be accurately identified by such means on vaccination certificates. Identification documents are used for racehorses and for animals transported abroad for competitive sports.

The descriptions of colours and markings in this book are based on those currently used by the Royal College of Veterinary Surgeons. The aim of this book is to provide the basic information to enable anyone to describe the coat colour and markings of horses. It can be used by veterinarians, agriculturists, horse owners and the horse-loving public in general, providing a guide for the student and allowing the pony club member to determine the colour and markings of his mount.

The book is in five parts, covering the descriptions of coat colours, body markings, head markings, limb markings and information on how to complete horse identification documents.

Throughout the book references are made to terms which previously were commonly used to describe colours and markings. Sometimes these terms were ambiguous and for the sake of conciseness and uniformity many terms are now redefined or discontinued. Therefore some names are mentioned which should now be disused and this fact is stressed.

CONTENTS

Plate 1

Points of the Horse

1. Forehead
2. Face
3. Muzzle
4. Chin
5. Cheek
6. Jugular groove
7. Neck
8. Shoulder
9. Point of shoulder
10. Breast
11. Chestnut
12. Coronet
13. Pastern
14. Fetlock
15. Forecannon
16. Knee
17. Forearm
18. Elbow
19. Brisket
20. Girth line
21. Barrel
22. Belly
23. Sheath
24. Stifle
25. Gaskin
26. Wall of hoof
27. Heel
28. Fetlock
29. Hind cannon
30. Hock
31. Thigh
32. Buttock
33. Tail
34. Dock
35. Croup
36. Point of hip
37. Flanks
38. Loins
39. Back
40. Withers
41. Mane
42. Crest
43. Poll
44. Forelock

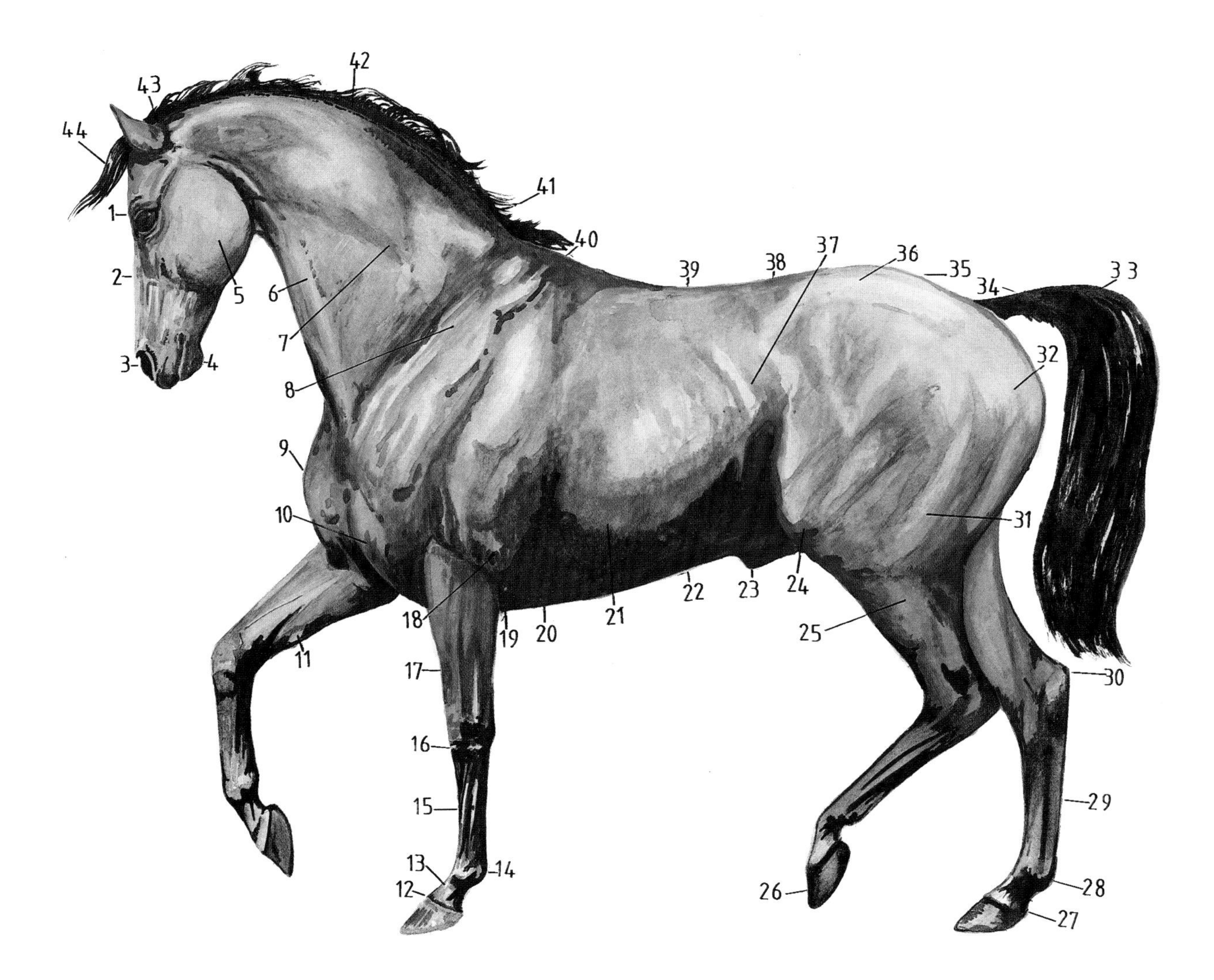
1
2
3
4
5
6
7
8
9
10
11
12
13
14
15
16
17
18
19
20
21
22
23
24
25
26
27
28
29
30
31
32
33
34
35
36
37
38
39
40
41
42
43
44

Plate 2

The Head of the Horse

1. Poll
2. Forelock
3. Forehead
4. Supraorbital fossa
5. Face
6. Bridge of nose
7. Muzzle
8. Nostril
9. Upper lip
10. Lower lip
11. Chin
12. Chin (or curb) groove
13. Lower jaw
14. Facial crest (cheek bone)
15. Cheek
16. Throat
17. Neck

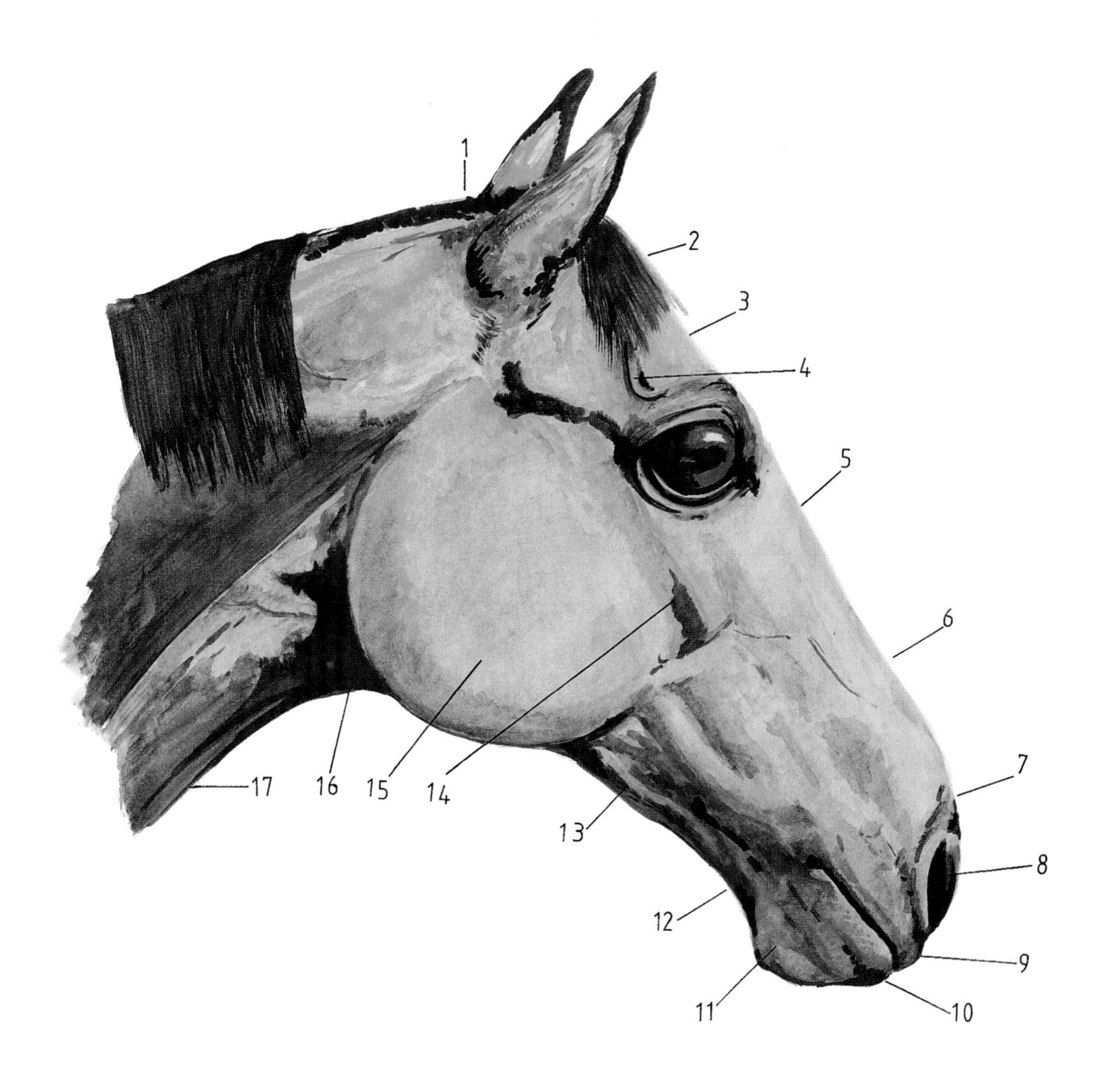
1
2
3
4
5
6
7
8
9
10
11
12
13
14
15
16
17

Part 1

BODY COLOURS

There are four basic coat colours in horses. These are black, brown, bay and chestnut. These coat colours are further added to by the effects of greying, roaning, dilution and spotting of the coat. In the case of animals with body coats consisting solely of white hairs the coat colour is categorised as grey or albino depending on the colour of the skin and the eyes (plate 12).

The various coat colours of horses are illustrated in the following series of plates (nos. 3–12) which are accompanied by descriptions of the coat colours.

It should be noted that where there is any doubt as to the colour of the animal the muzzle should be carefully examined and a decision based on the colour of the hairs found there.

Plate 3

Black, Brown and Bay

1. Black
The skin, mane, tail and body hair of the horse are black. No other colour is present except that white markings on the face and limbs are permitted.

2. Brown
The skin is dark with the coat hairs a mixture of black and chocolate with no yellow hairs. The limbs, mane and tail are black.

3. Bay brown
The main coat colour is brown with black limbs, mane and tail and a bay muzzle.

4. Bay
The coat is dark red to yellowish-brown in colour and the mane, tail and lower limbs are black. Black on the limbs is referred to as black points.

1
2
3
4

Plate 4

Bays

The coat of a bay horse can vary in shade from a dull reddish-brown to a yellowish-brown colour. The mane and tail are always black as are the lower limbs, and the tips of the ears may also be black.

The range in coat colour of bay horses resulted in the use of many descriptive names such as blood bay and sandy bay. Some examples of the shades of bay are illustrated and the commonly used descriptive name for that coat colour is given. However it is recommended that these terms are discontinued and for identification purposes only the term bay be used.

1. Light bay
Body coat a light yellowish-brown.

2. Golden bay
Body coat a golden yellow.

3. Red bay
Body coat a reddish-brown.

4. Dark Bay
Body coat a dark reddish-brown.

1
3

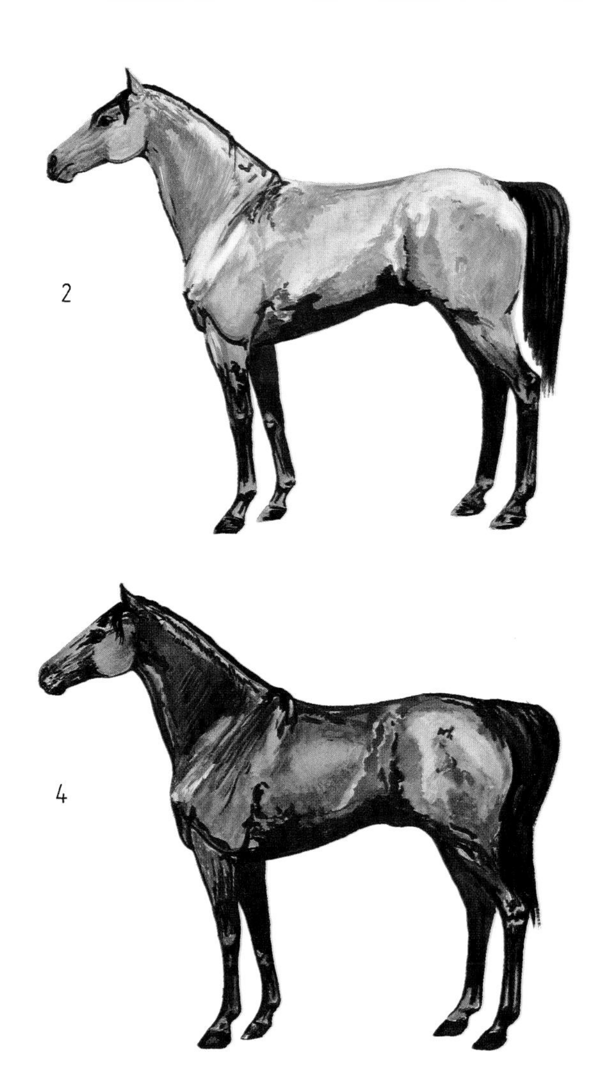
2
4

Plate 5

Chestnut (1)

The chestnut horse has yellow hairs in the coat. The proportion of yellow hair varies such as to give a coat which ranges in colour from reddish-brown to a light yellowish-brown. The colour can be lighter on the lower limbs, and the mane and tail can be a few shades darker or lighter than the body. If the mane and tail differ in colour from the body the difference should be noted.

Because of the range of colour found in chestnut horses it may be considered worth noting the intensity of coat colour. However it is desirable to avoid the use of colloquial terms in doing so. On plates 5 and 6 chestnut horses are illustrated and the commonly used descriptive name for the coat colour precedes the more appropriate term.

1. Bright chestnut (chestnut)
Body coat a bright yellowish-red.

2. Red chestnut (chestnut)
Body coat a reddish-brown colour.

3. Golden chestnut (light chestnut)
Body coat a bright yellowish-brown.

4. Liver chestnut (dark chestnut)
Body coat a very dark reddish-brown colour.

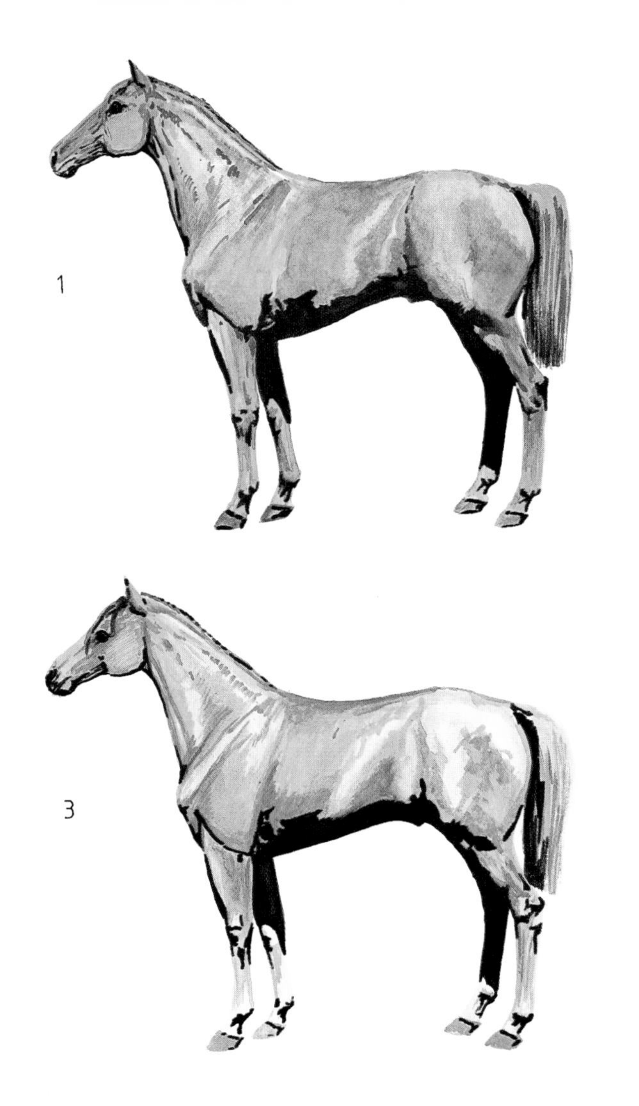
1
3

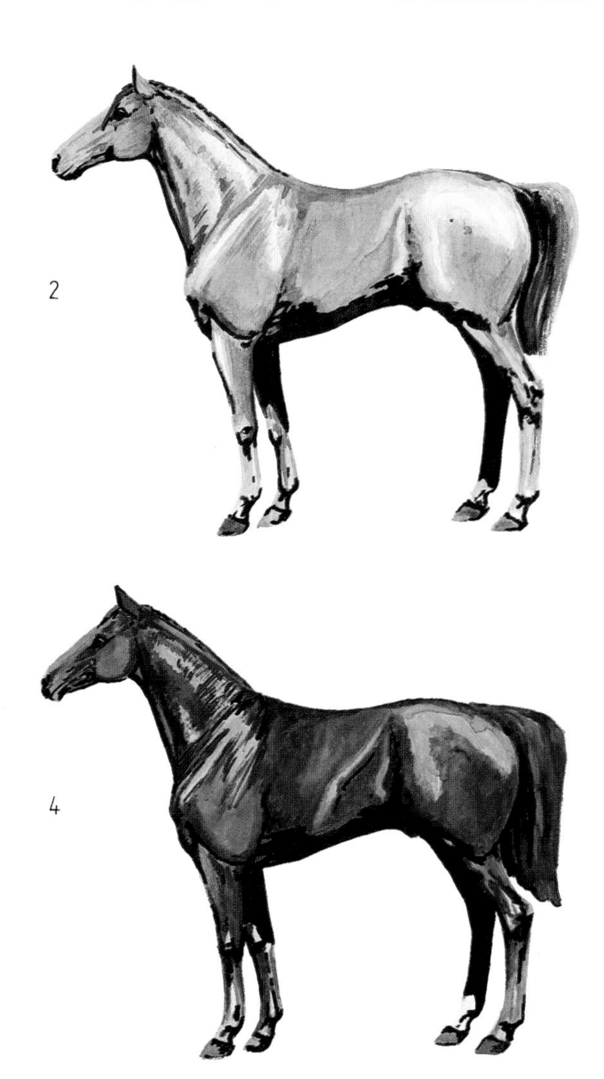
2
4

Plate 6

Chestnut (2)

1. Sorrel (light chestnut)
The coat colour is a light reddish-brown.

2. Chestnut with flaxen mane and tail
The body coat colour is chestnut with the mane and tail cream in colour.

3. Liver chestnut (dark chestnut) with flaxen mane and tail
A dark chestnut coat with cream coloured mane and tail.

4. Palomino
Horses of this colour type have a body coat which approximates the colour of a newly minted gold coin. The mane and tail are white.

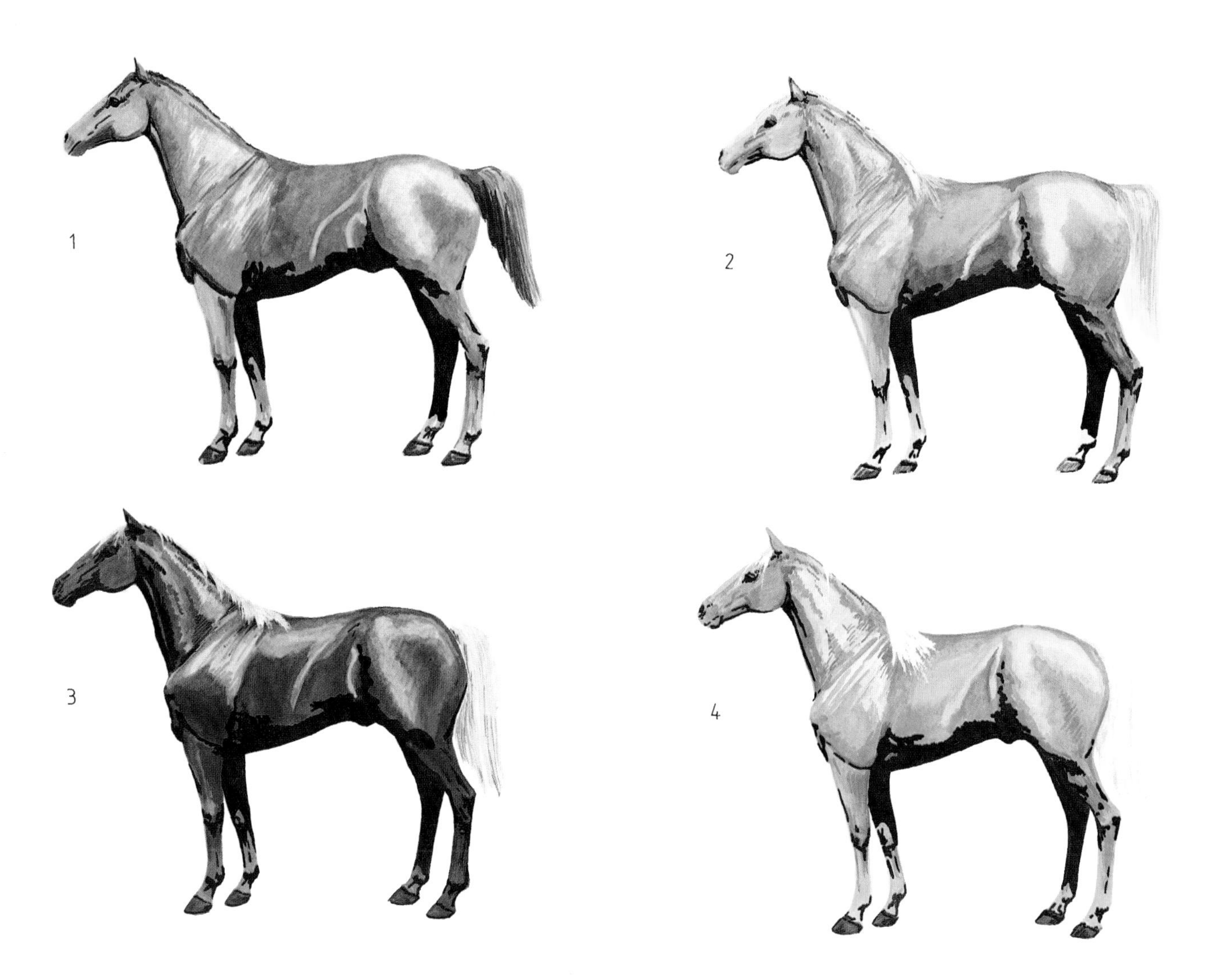

1
2
3
4

Plate 7

Duns

Dun colours are the result of a dilution of the basic coat colour.

1. Blue dun
The skin is black with the body colour a dilute black. The mane and tail are always black and there may be a dark dorsal stripe or list running from the base of the tail to the mane. A dark stripe may also be present down the withers.

2 and 3. Yellow dun
The skin is dark with the coat a diffuse yellow. The mane and tail may be black or chocolate. A withers stripe, list and zebra markings (dark bands on the legs) may be present.

4. Cream
The skin is unpigmented and the coat is a very light yellow. The eyes may be blue or pink.

1
2
3
4

Plate 8

Roans

A roan horse has a body coat which consists of a mixture of white and coloured hairs in equal quantities. The solid colour tends to predominate on the head and limbs and the colour of the roan is determined from this.

The roan differs from the grey horse which has a coat consisting of an uneven mixture of white and coloured hairs and where the percentage of white increases with age.

1. Bay or red roan
The body coat colour is bay or bay brown with an admixture of white hairs which results in a reddish tinge to the coat. Black hairs usually predominate on the lower limbs.

2. Chestnut or strawberry roan
The coat consists of equal proportions of white and chestnut giving a pink colour. Chestnut predominates on the lower limbs.

3. Blue roan
The coat has a blue tinge which is the result of an equal mixture of white and black or black–brown hairs.

4. Dark grey
The skin is dark and the coat is an uneven mixture of white and black or black–brown hairs. The percentage of white hairs increases with age and white tends to predominate on the face.

1
2
3
4

Plate 9

Greys

The coat of a grey horse is an uneven mixture of white and dark-coloured hairs with the skin darkly pigmented. As the animal ages the coat becomes lighter as the percentage of white hairs increases. The change in seasons can also result in changes in the shade of the coat. The mane and tail may be the same colour as the coat or may be lighter or darker in colour.

Because of the variations found in greys colloquial and common names were used to describe the colours and it is now recommended that all such horses are described as grey.

1. Iron grey
The coat colour is blue–grey.

2. Dapple grey
This is a term still in common use to describe a coat spotted in two shades of grey. It should be discontinued as the amount of dappling varies with season.

3. Flea-bitten grey
Grey body with small flecks of coloured hairs distributed through the coat. If this term is used it should be accompanied by a statement of the colours involved as it may be that more than two colours are present in the coat.

4. Light grey

For identification documents the colour of the hooves and any markings thereon should be described together with the presence of any whorls or acquired marks.

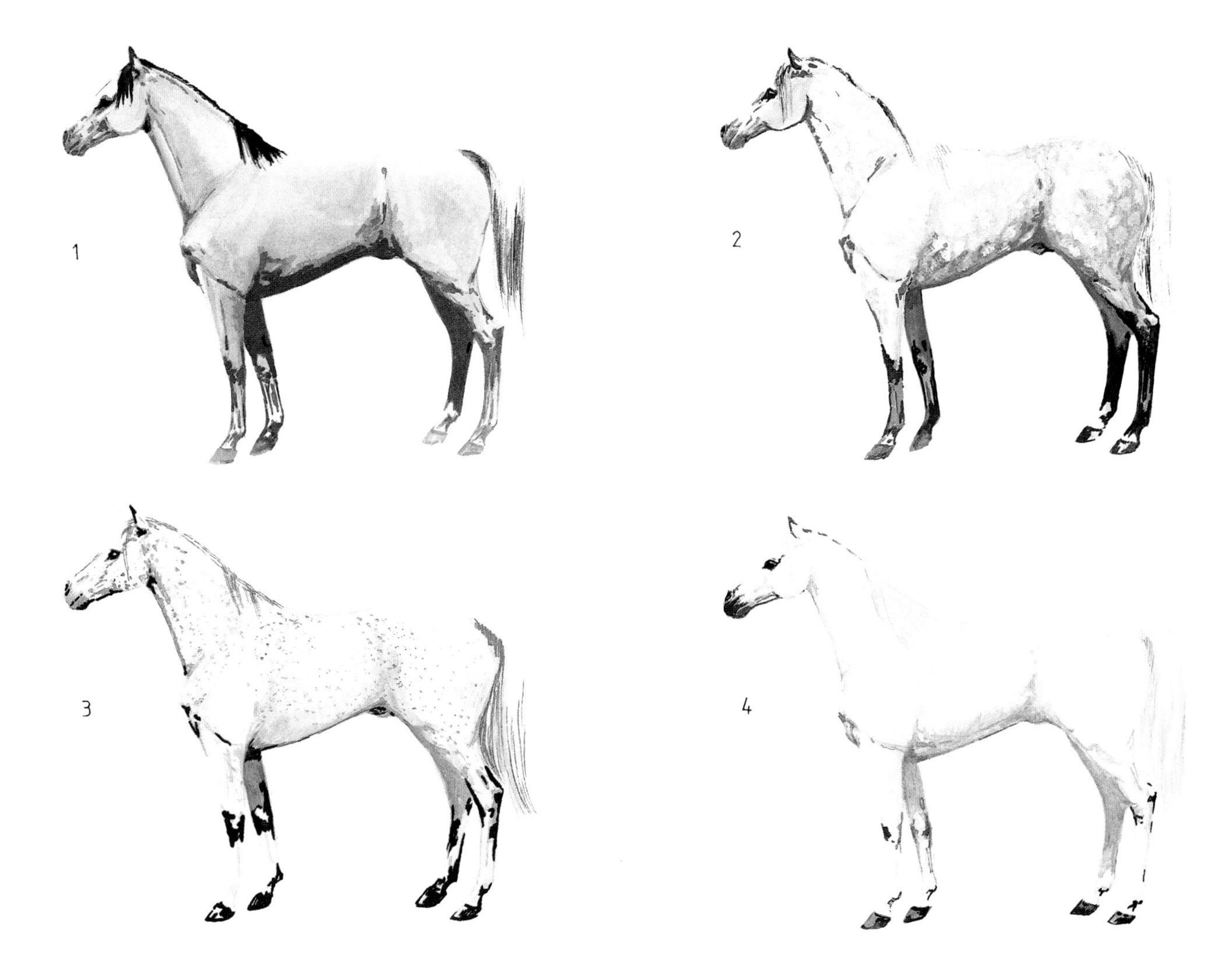
1
2
3
4

Plate 10

Pinto (Skewbald, Piebald, Odd-coloured)

1 and 2. Skewbalds
The coat consists of large irregular patches of white and any other colour except black. The line of demarcation between the patches is usually well defined.

3. Piebald
The coat consists of large irregular patches of white and black. The patches are well defined.

4. Odd-coloured
The coat consists of irregular patches of white and more than one other colour. The patches merge into one another and cannot be classified under skewbald or piebald.

The above terms are British. In the United States horses with such coats as this are termed pinto or paint and are recognised as a colour type. The pinto is categorised into two groups on the basis of the coat pattern as follows:

Overo pattern (no. 1 on plate)
Body colour is basically dark with white markings. White does not cross the back; one or more legs are dark, and there is a lot of white on the face. The tail is usually one colour and the patches are irregularly spotted.

Tobiano pattern (nos. 2, 3 and 4 on plate)
Body is basically white with coloured patches. White crosses the back; all the legs are white, at least below the knee or hock, and one or both flanks are dark. The body spots are large and regular, and the face is coloured or coloured with facial markings.

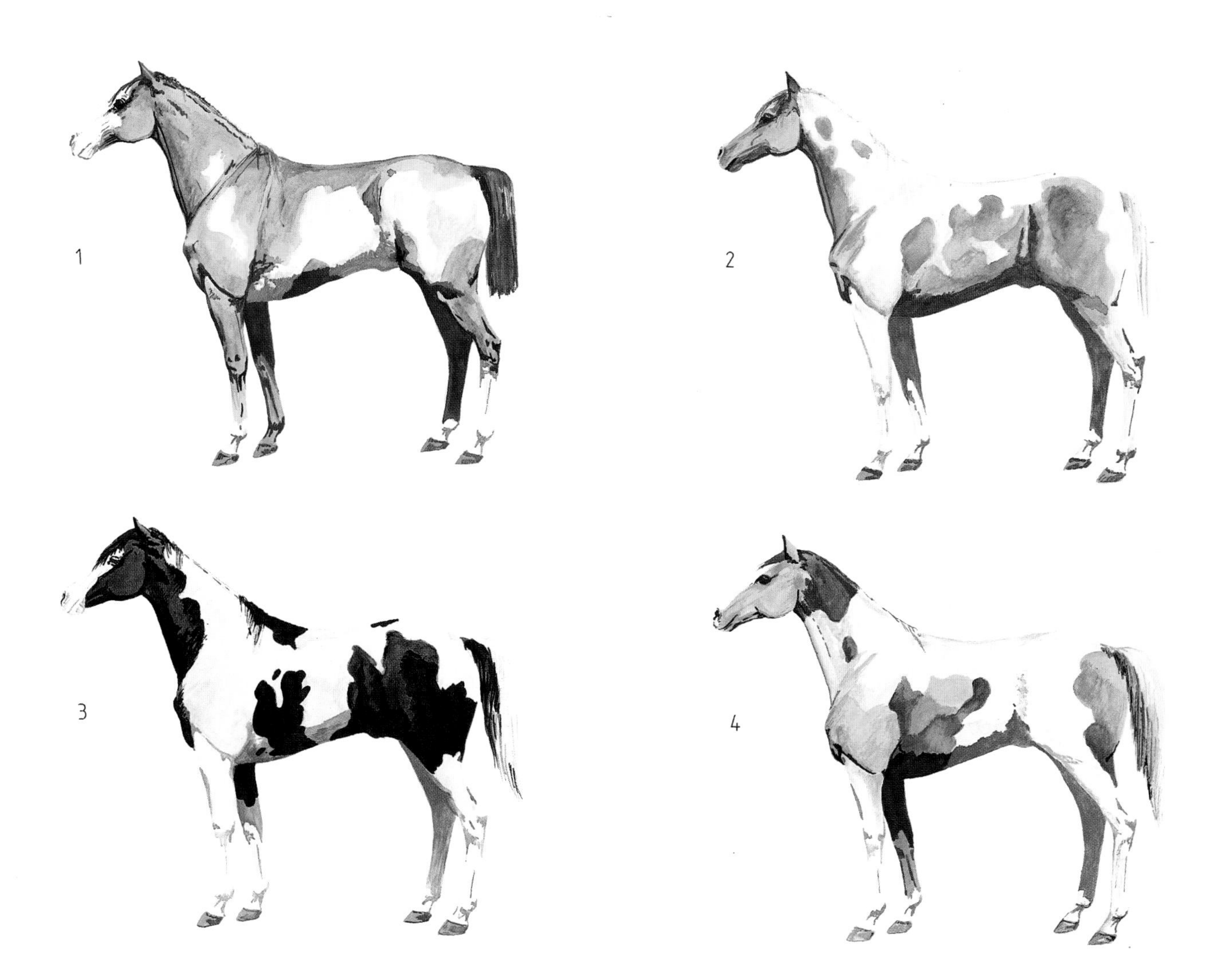
1
2
3
4

Plate 11

Appaloosa

The Appaloosa is a breed of horse originating in the United States and famous for the pattern variations of the coat. All true Appaloosa horses have a mottled skin, white around the eye and hooves which are vertically striped in black and white; the mane and tail are sparse. There are many variations in the coat pattern and four common patterns are illustrated here. These horses are often crossed with other breeds to carry over the coat pattern and appaloosian is a term used for an animal with a grey coat covered with a mosaic of black or brown spots.

1. Leopard pattern
Dark spots on a white coat. The spots are round or oval and can be up to 10 cm in diameter.

2. White blanket over back and hips
Here a white blanket on a chestnut horse is shown.

3. White blanket over back and hips with dark spots on the blanket
This is illustrated by a white blanket marking on a bay coat with black spots on the blanket.

4. Coloured body (bay in illustration) showing roaning with dark spots over back, hips and neck with no white blanket.

Other coat patterns are:

Snowflake: spotting all over the body but dominant over the hips.

Frost: white flecks on a dark coat.

Marbelised: mottled all over the body.

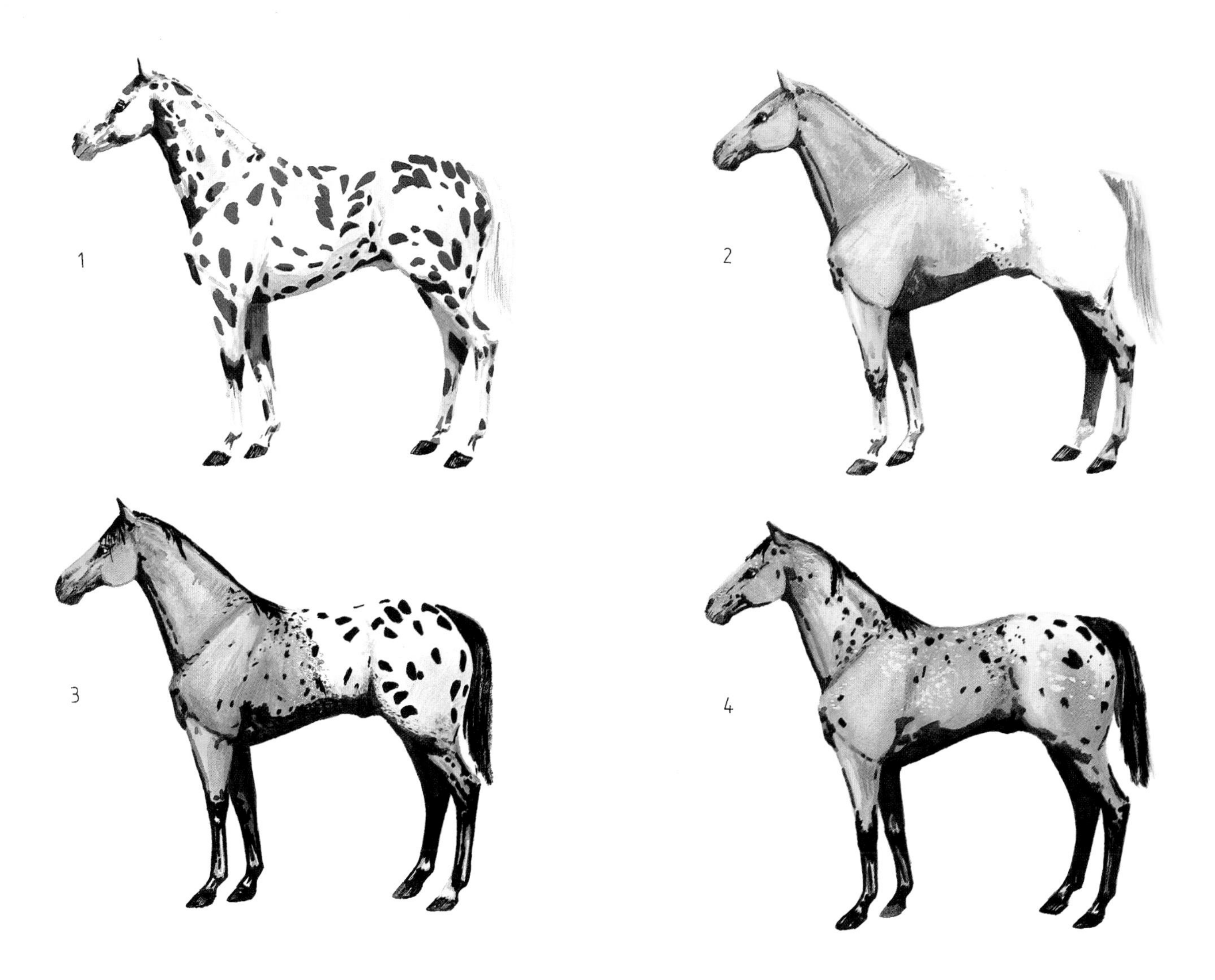
1
2
3
4

Plate 12

Grey, White and Albino

This plate illustrates the differences between the grey, white and albino coat colour. These differences are most noticeable on the head.

1. Grey
The skin is dark, the eyes are pigmented and the body hair a mixture of white and coloured hairs.

2. Albino
There is no pigmentation of the skin or hair. The eyes are also devoid of pigment and are pink in colour.

3. White
The skin is light and the hair is white. The eye is pigmented. White horses are rare; white as a coat colour is not recognised in some countries where horses which appear to be white are termed grey.

1
2
3

Part 2

BODY MARKINGS

There are several terms which may be used to distinguish markings on the body other than head and limb markings.

Grey-ticked
This refers to isolated white hairs sparsely distributed throughout the coat on any part of the body.

Flecked
Small areas of white hairs on any part of the body. The amount of flecking may be described by the terms heavily flecked or lightly flecked.

Spots
Small, rounded collections of hairs differing in colour from the rest of the body. The colour of the spots must be stated.

Patch
Any well-defined irregular area of colour differing from the general coat colour. The colour, shape and position of the patch should be described.

Black marks
Small areas of black hairs on any other colour.

Zebra marks
Striping on the limbs, neck, withers or quarters.

Flesh marks
Patches where the pigment of the skin is absent.

List
A dorsal band of black hairs which extends from the withers backwards.

Whorls

A whorl is formed by changes in the direction of flow of the hair and may take a variety of forms. Various types of whorl are as follows.

Simple: a point into which hairs converge from various directions.

Tufted: a whorl as above but the hair piles up into a tuft.

Linear: hairs from two opposite directions meet along a line.

Crested: as for linear but, on meeting, the hairs rise up.

Feathered: hairs from two directions meet along a line but at an angle so that a feathered pattern is formed.

Sinuous: hairs from two directions meet along an irregular curving line.

Whorls present on the head and neck should always be described and the presence of whorls can be used to identify an animal from its birth. The position and number of whorls varies from animal to animal but remains constant whereas colour may change with age (for instance in the grey horse). In the case of animals with no white markings at least five head, neck and body whorls are noted on identification documents.

General Terms

Whole coloured
This term means that there are no hairs of any other colour on the body, head or limbs.

Mixed
Used to describe a marking consisting of the general colour mixed with many white or lighter coloured hairs.

Bordered
Used to describe a marking which is circumscribed by an area of mixed colour.

Feathering
This refers to profuse long silky hairs on the fetlocks and which may extend up the back and sides of the cannon. It is characteristic of some pony and draught breeds and may be specified in breed registration requirements.

Dappling
This term, used to describe the mottled pattern on the coat resulting from a mosaic of two shades of hair, should be discontinued. The coat pattern can vary with age and season and therefore is not a reliable characteristic to use for identification purposes.

The Prophet's Thumb Mark
This is the name given to a muscular depression most commonly seen on the neck but also found on the shoulders and hindquarters. It is often found on animals of Arabian stock and Thoroughbreds.

Part 3

LIMB MARKINGS

At birth the hoof is usually white and attains the adult colour as the animal matures. White markings on the limbs were previously referred to as socks or stockings. A sock was a white marking to the middle of the cannon bone and a stocking was any white marking which reached the knee or hock or above these joints.

Nowadays for the sake of uniformity the use of these terms is being discouraged. Any limb marking should be concisely described with reference to the extent of the marking on the inside and outside of the limb. It was common practice to refer to the left side of the horse as the near side, this being the side from which the rider mounts the animal. The right side of the horse was called the off side. The limbs were then called near foreleg, off foreleg, etc. Use of these terms is also discouraged and for description purposes the left and right side of the body should be so called and the limbs correspondingly named, i.e. left foreleg, etc.

Definitions of Limb Markings

White coronet
Hair immediately above the hoof is white.

White heel
The heel is the back of the pastern to the hoof. When the white marking is confined to one or both bulbs of the heel it should be noted.

White pastern
The pastern is that part of the leg from the fetlock downwards and the extent of the white should be described, for instance half pastern, three-quarter pastern.

White fetlock
White to the fetlock joint and any variation should be noted.

Higher white markings
The extent of the marking should be described, for instance white to the hock, white to halfway up the cannon.

Plates 13 and 14 illustrate common markings of the fore and hind legs respectively. It is necessary on a description document to give any variation in the marking on the inside and outside of the limb and a combination of terms may be used. Any variation in the colour of the hooves should also be described and in the case of an animal with few identifying characteristics the colour of the individual hooves should be specified.

Plate 13

Markings on the Foreleg

1. White fleck on the coronet.
2. White heel.
3. White coronet.
4. White pastern.
5. White to the fetlock.
6. White to halfway up the cannon.
7. White to just below the knee.
8. White to halfway up the forearm.
9. White to halfway up the cannon. Three black flecks on the coronet.

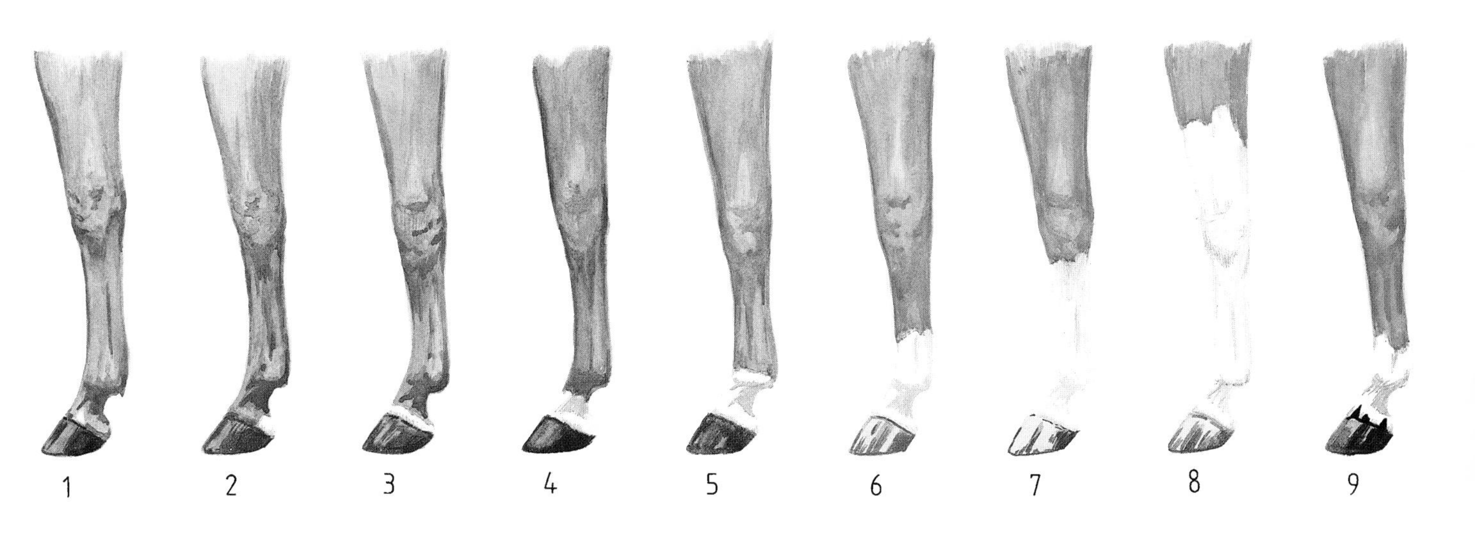
1
2
3
4
5
6
7
8
9

Plate 14

Markings on the Hindleg

1. White heel.
2. White coronet.
3. White pastern.
4. White to above fetlock.
5. White to the top of the cannon.
6. White up to and including the hock.
7. White up to the gaskin.
8. White to halfway up the cannon. Three black flecks on the coronet.

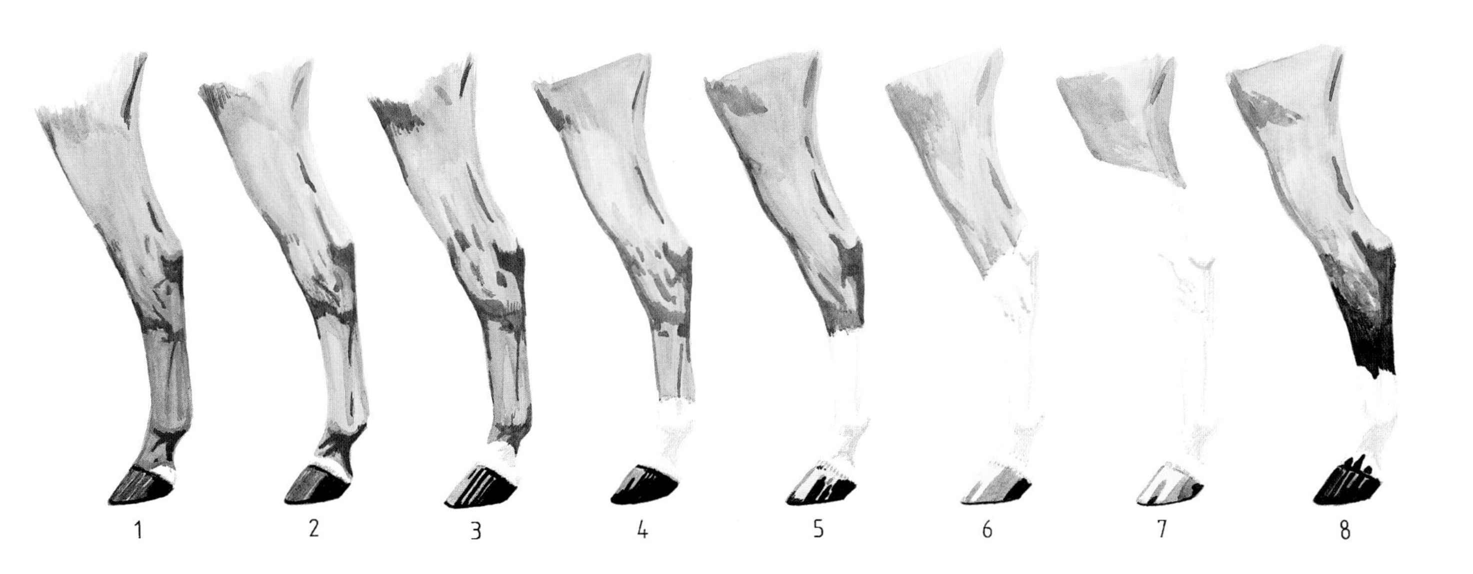
1
2
3
4
5
6
7
8

Part 4

HEAD MARKINGS

Head markings are covered by a variety of terms. The marking on a particular animal may be described by the use of a single term or it may be necessary to use a combination of terms. In all cases a full description of the extent of a marking should be given on a description document.

Definitions of Head Markings

Star
A white mark on the forehead. The shape, position, size and intensity of the marking should be given and any coloured area on the white should be described.

Stripe
This covers the narrow white marking down the centre of the face and which does not extend over the width of the nasal bones. The width, length, direction and point of termination of the stripe should be given and any coloured marking on the white described. A stripe may be a continuation of a star and in this case the marking is described as a star and stripe conjoined. When a star and stripe are separate this is described as a star and interrupted stripe. (Plates 19, 20 and 25.)

Blaze
A white marking covering the forehead and extending down the face covering the whole width of the nasal bones. Any variation in width and direction to be specified. Termination of the blaze and any coloured markings on the white to be specified. (Plates 20–22.)

White face
White covers the forehead and the front of the face and extends laterally towards the mouth. The full extent of the white on each side of the

face should be described and any coloured markings on the white specified. (Plates 26 and 27.)

Snip
An independent white marking between, or in the region of, the nostrils. The position and size to be described. (Plate 24.)

Lip markings
The colour, size and position of any marking on the lips should be fully described. (Plates 23 and 25.)

White muzzle
White over both lips to the region of the nostrils. (Plate 23.)

Eyes

Any variation in the normal pigmentation of the eye is a useful feature of note in the description of an animal. The pink eye of the albino and any other variations in colour should be noted. The two following terms are used.

Wall-eye
Used to describe lack of pigment in the iris. The eye is bluish-white or grey in colour. (Plates 26 and 27.)

Showing the white of the eye
Horses which show the sclera or white of the eye should be so described.

The following series of plates illustrates the variety of head markings to be seen on horses. Each plate is accompanied by a description of the markings illustrated.

Plate 15

Stars (1)

1. White hairs in the centre of the forehead.
2. Small star in the centre of the forehead.
3. Two small stars on the forehead above eye level (upper star to the right of the midline, lower to the left of the midline).
4. Small star at the top of the forehead.
5. Star in the middle of the forehead.

1
2
3
4
5

Plate 16

Stars (2)

1. Large star in the centre of the forehead.
2. Central elongated star extending to lower eye level.
3. Small star on the top of the forehead to the right of the midline and a small elongated star below to the lower eye level.
4. Elongated star, horizontal across the forehead, above upper eye level.
5. Crescent-shaped star turned to the right in the centre of the forehead. (A crescent shape to the left should be so described.)

1
2
3
4
5

Plate 17

Stars (3)

1. Heart-shaped star in the middle of the forehead.
2. Triangular star extending down the middle of the forehead and ending at the lower eye level.
3. Large triangular star extending from the top of the forehead to below the lower eye level.
4. Star in the centre of the forehead, conjoined triangular-shaped stripe from lower eye level to the centre of the face.
5. Large irregular star, three indentations on top edge, narrowing to end at the top of the face.

1
2
3
4
5

Plate 18

Stars (4)

1. Large irregular dentate star in the centre of the forehead.
2. Large bordered oval star in the middle of the forehead.
3. Small bordered dentate star, middle of the forehead at eye level.
4. Large oval star with four coloured flecks on the white.
5. Large mixed star.

1
2
3
4
5

Plate 19

Stripes (1)

1. Narrow stripe in the centre of the face.
2. Small star conjoined narrow stripe to the top of the muzzle.
3. Small star conjoined narrow stripe broadening at the bottom of the face and ending on the top of the muzzle.
4. Narrow stripe to right of midline from below eye level to the bottom of the face; six coloured flecks on the white.
5. Narrow mixed stripe to right of midline extending from the top to the bottom of the face.

1
2
3
4
5

Plate 20

Stripes and Blazes (1)

1. Small star interrupted broad stripe to the top of the muzzle. Ending on the left of the muzzle.
2. Star conjoined broad stripe to the top of the muzzle. The stripe narrowing in the centre of the face.
3. Star conjoined stripe to the right of the midline ending in the right nostril.
4. Star conjoined broad stripe to the top of the muzzle.
5. Blaze ending on upper lip.

1
2
3
4
5

Plate 21

Stripes and Blazes (2)

1. Triangular-shaped blaze, point to right of midline at the top of the muzzle.
2. Wide blaze entering both nostrils and ending on the upper lip.
3. Blaze, wide on forehead narrowing on top of the face then broadening to end in both nostrils.
4. Broad stripe from top to bottom of face.
5. Blaze, irregular edge on forehead with an indentation on the left at the lower eye level. Ending on the top of the muzzle.

1
2
3
4
5

Plate 22

Stripes and Blazes (3)

1. Broad bordered blaze to the muzzle.
2. Broad blaze to the top of the muzzle, coloured spot on midline at lower eye level. Spot to left of midline in the centre of the face and another to the right of midline below this.
3. Blaze narrowing on the face and inclining to enter the left nostril.
4. Blaze to muzzle, oval mixed patch in the centre of the face.
5. Broad stripe from the middle of the face widening at the bottom of the face to enter right nostril and ending on top of the upper lip.

1
2
3
4
5

Plate 23

Lip and Muzzle Markings

1. White spot on the left of the lower lip.
2. Lower lip white.
3. Upper and lower lips white.
4. White muzzle.
5. White muzzle with coloured flecks throughout the white. Left eye a wall eye and a ring of white encircling the eye.

1

2

3

4

5

Plate 24

Snips and Muzzle Markings

1. Small white snip to the left on the bottom of the muzzle.
2. Large white snip on the bottom right of the muzzle.
3. Large white snip on the upper lip. White entering the right nostril and extending to the top of the muzzle.
4. White snip on the right of the upper lip.
5. Narrow stripe from middle of face broadening to end on the upper lip; white entering both nostrils.

1
2
3
4
5

Plate 25

Combined Markings

1. Large oval star conjoined narrow stripe to the bottom of the face.
2. Small star, interrupted narrow stripe to the bottom of the face. Irregular white snip on muzzle, white entering right nostril and extending below left nostril.
3. Elongated irregular star down centre of forehead. Large triangular white snip, white extending from upper lip to a point on the top of the muzzle and passing below both nostrils.
4. Large triangular star, interrupted narrow stripe to the bottom of the face. Small elongated white snip near right nostril and a triangular white snip on upper lip to the left of the midline, point reaching to lower level of nostrils.
5. Dentate star, conjoined bordered stripe down the left side of the face broadening into solid white at top of nostril and ending on left side of upper lip.

1
2
3
4
5

Plate 26

White Face, Combined Markings (1)

1(a, b). White face with wall-eyes.

White extending bilaterally over forehead to encircle the eyes. White to the cheekbones then extending to cover the mouth and the lower jaw.

2(a, b). Diamond-shaped star conjoined broad stripe widening bilaterally on face to encompass both nostrils and the chin.

3(a, b). Bordered white face, left eye a wall-eye.

White extending bilaterally from the top of the forehead to the eyes. Left eye encircled with white which extends to the cheekbone, white touching orbit and cheekbone on the right. Lower side of face and nostril on the right white. White narrowing on left to just enter the left nostril. White ending on muzzle. White flecking on upper lip. Large oval spot and white flecking on left side of chin.

1a
2a
3a
1b
2b
3b

Plate 27

White Face, Combined Markings (2)

1. Irregular broad blaze to the muzzle, white entering the right nostril and just touching the left nostril. Sides of face white.
2. Large crescent star to the right, conjoined broad stripe to the muzzle. White entering the right nostril.
3. Irregular blaze narrowing to end as a point on bottom of the muzzle. White above left eye and indentations into white on sides of face. White touching the left nostril and entering the right.
4. White face ending on muzzle. Left eye a wall-eye. White over the left eye and top of left cheek white. Right side of face white. Large white rectangular snip in centre on the bottom of the muzzle, bottom lip white.
5. White face with wall-eyes. White extending irregularly from the centre of the top of the forehead to the upper eye level, white around left eye. White extending bilaterally from lower eye level to encompass cheeks and sides of face. Right nostril and top of left nostril white. Triangular white spot above left eye. Six spots on the white in the region of the forehead and upper face.

1
2
3
4
5

Plate 28

Adventitious Markings

Some markings are not congenital and are the result of accidents, branding or scarring. Markings resulting from the wear of harness (e.g. bridle mark, girth mark), brands, tattoos and any other adventitious marks should be described on an identification document.

This plate illustrates some common adventitious marks:

1. Bridle marks (face, cheek and poll).
2. Saddle marks.
3. Girth marks.
4. Hobble marks.

Also illustrated is a congenital marking:

5. Flesh mark. A patch where the pigment of the skin is absent.

1
1
5
2
2
3
5
4

Part 5

COMPLETION OF IDENTIFICATION DOCUMENTS

The following gives the method of completing the identification certificate (figure 1).

Any white marking on the horse must be shown in red ink; any other marks on the diagram must be completed in black ink. The use of ball-point pens is recommended because this ensures good results if the document is photocopied.

Starting with the head, define all markings ensuring that all whorls are indicated. Continue with the left side of the animal then the right, defining the limb markings and examining for any marks on the heels. The forelock should be raised to ensure that no whorls on the forehead are missed, likewise examination for whorls under the mane must be made.

The narrative and the completed diagram must agree.

Markings are indicated as follows:

Whorls

The position of whorls is indicated by a 'X' in the case of simple or tufted whorls.

Linear or feathered whorls are indicated by placing 'X' where the whorl starts and a straight line from this to indicate the direction and extent of the whorl.

A sinuous whorl is indicated by a 'X' and an 'S'-shaped line from this to show the full extent of the whorl.

The type of whorl must be stated in the accompanying text.

Head whorls

These should be indicated on the diagram and described precisely in the narrative. Attention should be paid to their position relative to the eye level, midline or any white markings on the head.

Body whorls

The neck should be divided into anterior, middle and posterior sections to facilitate the indication and description of whorls on the neck or crest of the horse. Body whorls should be indicated as accurately as possible referring to the anatomy of the animal.

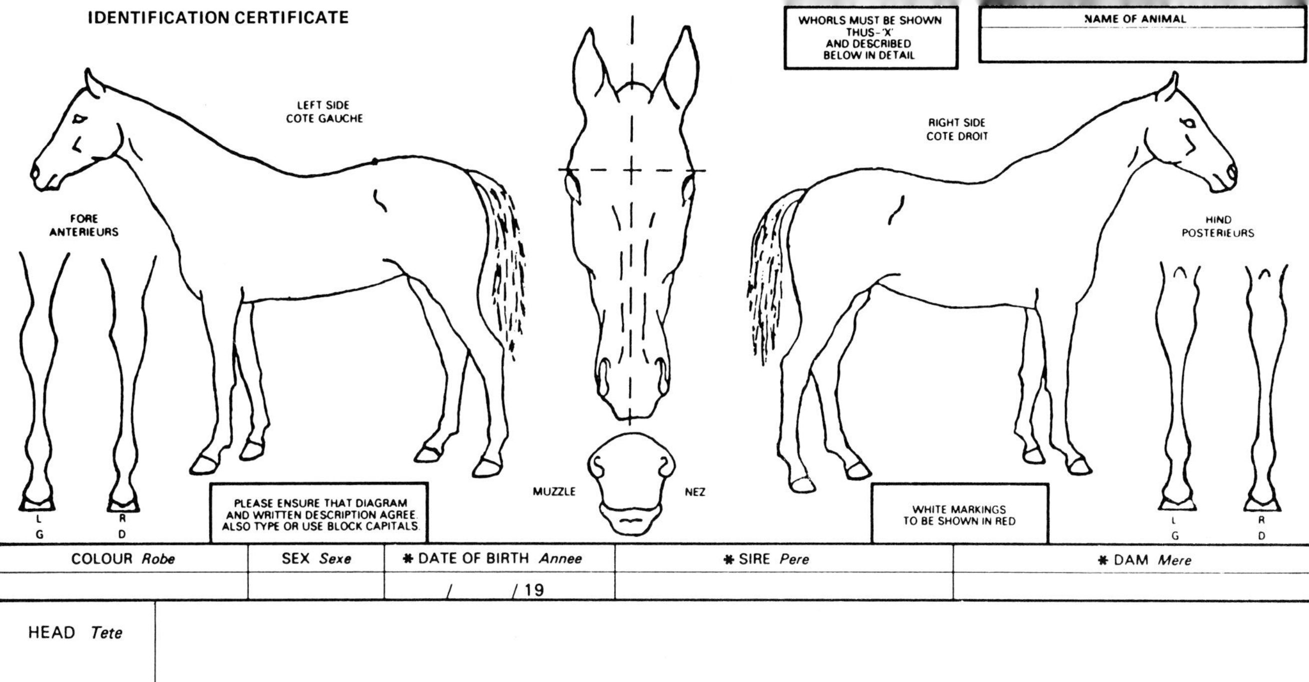

COLOUR *Robe*	SEX *Sexe*	✱ DATE OF BIRTH *Annee*	✱ SIRE *Pere*	✱ DAM *Mere*
		/ / 19		

HEAD *Tete*	
Jambes LIMBS LF	
RF	
LH	
RH	
BODY *Corps*	
ACQUIRED *Marques Acquises*	

Figure 1

DATE OF EXAMINATION ....

SIGNATURE of Veterinary Surgeon ....
(Not to be the breeder owner, or trainer of the horse for which the certificate is issued)

NAME AND ADDRESS ....
(in block capitals)
....

THIS IS NOT A NAME REGISTRATION FORM

✱ These 3 items are based on information supplied by the Owner or their Agent.

White markings
These are outlined in red and lightly hatched in with diagonal lines. A few white hairs may be indicated by a few short lines in red. Care must be taken not to obliterate any whorl which is present within the marking.

A bordered marking
Indicate by using a double line.

Mixed marking
Indicate as for a white marking but the fact that it is mixed must be stated in the description.

Spot
A white spot should be indicated as for a white marking. A spot within a white marking should be outlined and left blank using black ball-point.

Flesh mark
Outline and shade in completely with red. Any spots on the mark should be outlined in black and left unshaded.

Bordered flesh mark
Indicate by a double line and shade in the inner demarcation with red.

Black spots or marks
Black spots or marks on the coat should be outlined in black and left unshaded. If extensive and numerous the markings should be noted only in the description.

Scars
Describe in the narrative and indicate on the diagram by an arrow.

The Prophet's Thumb Mark
Indicate on the diagram by a triangle and state in the description.

Others
Indicate white hairs in the mane and tail by red lines. White marks from freeze branding, surgery, etc., indicate as for white markings.

Hairs of a different colour on parts of the coat should be described with accuracy and indicated with a few diagonal lines.

If the horse is docked or the ears nicked it should be stated in the description.

Completed standard horse identification documents are shown in figures 2 and 3.

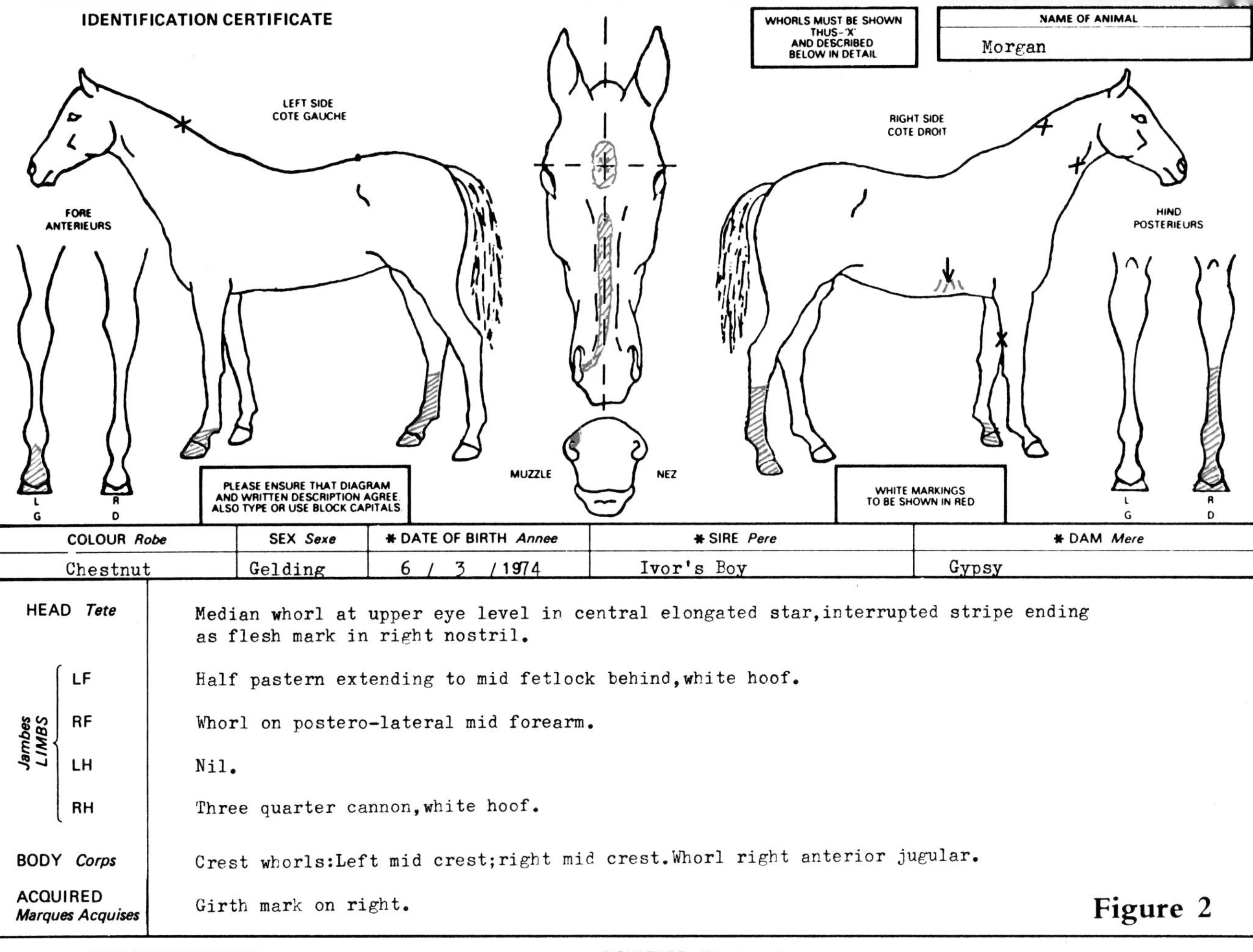

IDENTIFICATION CERTIFICATE

WHORLS MUST BE SHOWN THUS–'X' AND DESCRIBED BELOW IN DETAIL

NAME OF ANIMAL: Morgan

LEFT SIDE / COTE GAUCHE

RIGHT SIDE / COTE DROIT

FORE / ANTERIEURS

HIND / POSTERIEURS

L G   R D

MUZZLE   NEZ

PLEASE ENSURE THAT DIAGRAM AND WRITTEN DESCRIPTION AGREE. ALSO TYPE OR USE BLOCK CAPITALS.

WHITE MARKINGS TO BE SHOWN IN RED

COLOUR *Robe*	SEX *Sexe*	* DATE OF BIRTH *Annee*	* SIRE *Pere*	* DAM *Mere*
Chestnut	Gelding	6 / 3 / 1974	Ivor's Boy	Gypsy

HEAD *Tete*	Median whorl at upper eye level in central elongated star, interrupted stripe ending as flesh mark in right nostril.
Jambes LIMBS — LF	Half pastern extending to mid fetlock behind, white hoof.
RF	Whorl on postero-lateral mid forearm.
LH	Nil.
RH	Three quarter cannon, white hoof.
BODY *Corps*	Crest whorls: Left mid crest; right mid crest. Whorl right anterior jugular.
ACQUIRED *Marques Acquises*	Girth mark on right.

Figure 2

DATE OF EXAMINATION ....

SIGNATURE of Veterinary Surgeon ....
(Not to be the breeder owner, or trainer of the horse for which the certificate is issued)

THIS IS NOT A NAME REGISTRATION FORM

NAME AND ADDRESS (in block capitals) ....

* These 3 items are based on information supplied by the Owner or their Agent.

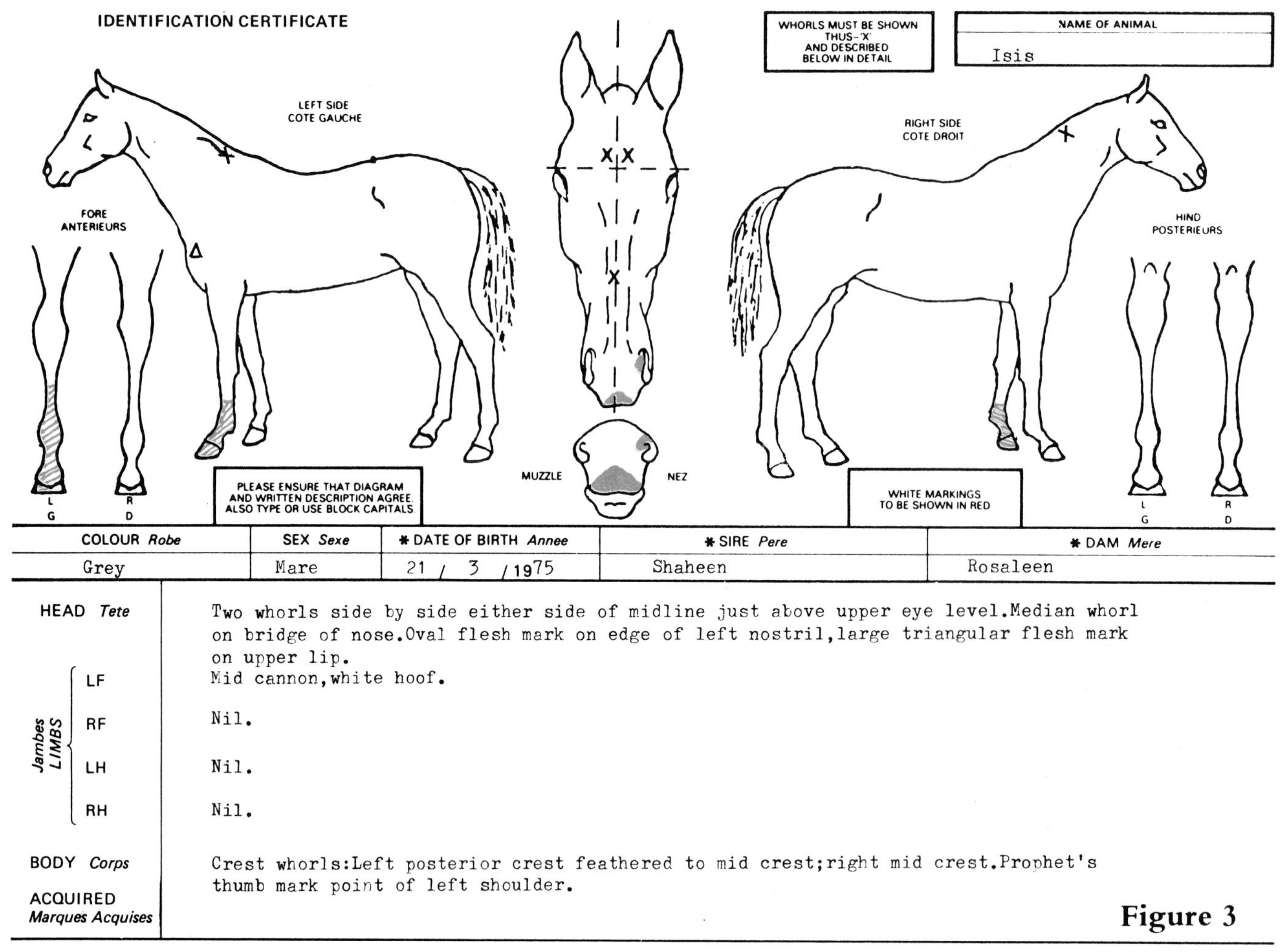

IDENTIFICATION CERTIFICATE

WHORLS MUST BE SHOWN THUS–'X' AND DESCRIBED BELOW IN DETAIL

NAME OF ANIMAL: Isis

LEFT SIDE / COTE GAUCHE

RIGHT SIDE / COTE DROIT

FORE / ANTERIEURS — L G — R D

HIND / POSTERIEURS — L G — R D

MUZZLE — NEZ

PLEASE ENSURE THAT DIAGRAM AND WRITTEN DESCRIPTION AGREE. ALSO TYPE OR USE BLOCK CAPITALS.

WHITE MARKINGS TO BE SHOWN IN RED

COLOUR *Robe*	SEX *Sexe*	* DATE OF BIRTH *Annee*	* SIRE *Pere*	* DAM *Mere*
Grey	Mare	21 / 3 / 1975	Shaheen	Rosaleen

HEAD *Tete*		Two whorls side by side either side of midline just above upper eye level. Median whorl on bridge of nose. Oval flesh mark on edge of left nostril, large triangular flesh mark on upper lip.
Jambes LIMBS	LF	Mid cannon, white hoof.
	RF	Nil.
	LH	Nil.
	RH	Nil.
BODY *Corps*		Crest whorls: Left posterior crest feathered to mid crest; right mid crest. Prophet's thumb mark point of left shoulder.
ACQUIRED *Marques Acquises*		

Figure 3

DATE OF EXAMINATION ....

SIGNATURE of Veterinary Surgeon ....
(Not to be the breeder owner, or trainer of the horse for which the certificate is issued)

NAME AND ADDRESS (in block capitals) ....

THIS IS NOT A NAME REGISTRATION FORM

* These 3 items are based on information supplied by the Owner or their Agent.